Comic Capers
MINNIE the MINX

BEANObooks
geddes & grosset

Danger! Minx at Work!
Minnie's Tartan Army

Published 2000 by BEANO books geddes & grosset ,
an imprint of Children's Leisure Products Limited,
David Dale House, New Lanark ML11 9DJ, Scotland

ISBN 1 84205 007 9

Printed and bound in Italy

PAH! I'LL SHOW THE OLD WINDBAG! JOB MARKET LOOK OUT!

AH! THE BUS.

THINK I'LL BECOME A BUS DRIVER!

ULP? SHE'S JUST JOKING, I THINK.

WE'RE NOT WAITING TO FIND OUT! FLEE!

AN' SHE'S NOT TOUCHING MY LOVELY BUS.

SNIGGER!

DRAT! HAVE TO HAIL A CAB NOW. TAXI!

OHO! ANOTHER JOB FOR ME.

ALL ABOARD MIN'S CABS!

AARGH!

NOT LIKELY!

MINNIECABS

SHORTLY—

YUS! WOT DO YOU WANT, MINX?

SORRY ABOUT THE LITTLE "ACCIDENT", OFFICER. I THOUGHT I'D MAKE IT UP TO YOU . . . YOU COULD ALWAYS USE A HAND . . .

. . . MEET W.P.C. MINNIE, AT YOUR SERVICE!

HOWL! WHY ME?

HO-HUM! BETTER HUMOUR HER I SUPPOSE.

BETTER STILL . . . PUT HER OFF! HEH!

YOU CAN BE IN CHARGE OF ANOTHER NEW RECRUIT. MEET POLICE DOG FLASH!

GRROWL!

MEN AT WORK

I WONDER WOT I COULD DO NEXT?

OW!

OW!

OW!

OI! YOU WOKE US UP!

OH! SORRY! I WAS LOOKING FOR A JOB.

YOU COULD DO OUR JOB DIGGIN' TRENCHES, IF YOU LIKE?

WOW! YOU BET! SOUNDS NEAT!

WORRA MUG!

YIPPEE!

TEA BREAK

THIS LOOKS LIKE WORK FOR A REAL MINX!

CHONKA!

YAARGH! STEADY ON, GIRL!

SPLAT!

SPLOSH!

WOTTSAT?

CHUNG!

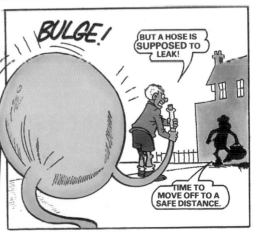

SNOOORP!

PULL!

NUMFFT!

ONE LAST DITCH EFFORT...

HUP!

OH! HE'S STUCK IN THE DRAIN, NOW!

SLUNK!

HEE-YAH! AN' OUT!

THAT'S UNBLOCKED IT... ALL OVER ME! YEUCH!

ENOUGH! A PLUMBERS LIFE IS NOT FOR ME!

I'LL HAVE TO HAVE IT AMPUTATED — OR I'LL STARVE!

CHAPTER THREE —
NO TAME DAME!

I'M A FAILURE!

BUT WAIT! THAT'S IT! I'LL RUN AWAY AND JOIN THE CIRCUS!

AND SO—

JUST THE JOB!

LION TAMER WANTED

I'LL TAME YOUR LIONS, RINGMASTER.

YOU? WHOO-HOO-HOO! DON'T MAKE ME LAFF, LITTLE GIRL! YOU'D MAKE A BRILL CLOWN THOUGH!

BAH!

I'LL SHOW YOU, MATE!

NO, WAIT! AT LEAST TAKE A WHIP AND CHAIR!

BAH! THANKS TO YOU, WE'VE NOTHING LEFT TO TAME.

NOTHING BEATS THE MINX!

HOW ABOUT GETTING HER TO TAME OUR CIRCUS FLEAS?

AH, YES!

TUG!

SEE WHAT YOU CAN DO WITH THOSE PERFORMING FLEAS. NO ONE'S BEEN ABLE TO TAME 'EM EVER!

PROD!

FLEAS? WHAT A DAWDLE!

RIGHT YOU FLEAS . . . JUST DO AS YOU'RE TOLD! THERE'S NO FLIES ON ME, Y'KNOW. HEH!

OH, YES THERE IS!

PING!

ERK! BACK! BACK, I SAY!

HOWL! MUST FLEE THE FLEAS!

SCRATCH!

HAW! HAW! HAPPENS EVERY TIME!

CHAPTER FOUR — MINNIE TAKES OVER!

AW! WHAT FOOL LEFT PITCH FORKS IN THE HAY?

GRR! YOU'VE REALLY BLOWN IT NOW, MINNIE!

PLOUGHING THE OLD WAY. USING MINX POWER! HEH!

HOI! WHATCHA DOIN'?

CRACK!

IF IT'S A JOB YOU WANT, IT'S A JOB YOU'LL GET!

WHEEZE! THIS IS SLAVERY! I WANNA BE ABOLISHED! A FARMER'S LOT IS NOT FOR ME!

SHORTLY —

THAT'S WHERE DAD WORKS. I WONDER . . .

JUST THEN —

HOW AM I SUPPOSED TO TYPE THIS? I CAN'T READ HIS AWFUL WRITING!

OHO!

BOSSFUL STRUT!

THROW!

I'M GONNA THROW THE BOOK AT YOU, MISS!

YIPE!

WULP!

SPITOO!

EEK! IT'S THE BOSS!

I'LL . . . I'LL . . . I'M SO MAD I DON'T KNOW WHERE TO START!

MERCY O' MASTER!

ALLOW ME TO DEAL WITH THE TWIT!

ER . . . OKAY!

Minnie's TARTAN ARMY

Chapter One – A HIGHLAND GATHERING.

I LOVE A A LITTLE SNACK AT BEDTIME . . .

. . . ESPECIALLY WHEN I'M RAVENOUS! GOBBLE! GORGE! CHOMP!

GLAAHK!

STOP STUFFING YOUR FACE THIS INSTANT, MINNIE!

TO BED! ALL THAT SCOFFING WILL GIVE YOU NIGHTMARES, GIRL.

NIGHT-NIGHT, DAD.

WHAT'S UP HER JUMPER!

GOTTA HELP! BUT HOW WILL I GET TO SCOTLAND?

A MESSENGER BROUGHT THAT LETTER . . . IF YOU HURRY YOU MIGHT CATCH HIM AND GET A LIFT.

CLEVER MUM.

YIPPEE! TO THE RESCUE!

HAGGIS EXPRESS

BONNIE SCOTLAND!

SCOTLAND

YOW! I TAKE IT WE'VE ARRIVED.

HAGGIS EXPRESS

Chapter Two – MINNIE GIVES UP THE GHOST!

OMINOUS RUMBLE!

ERK! SOUNDS LIKE WE'VE SET OFF AN AVALANCHE WITH THE SOUNDS OF BATTLE.

AARGH! ROCK FALL! WE'RE DOOMED!

McMINCE 'EM!

BLATT!

BOP!

EEK! IT'S THE MacFUDGES!

HAR! HAR! THIS IS JUST A WEE TASTE OF WHAT YOU'RE GONNA GET!

BOING! BOING!

THIS IS GONNA BE A HARDER TASK THAN I THOUGHT. MOAN!

PICKLED BEETROOT JUICE! MUCH BETTER!

SLOSH!

GLUBBS!

A BIT OF TOMATO SAUCE AS A FINAL TOUCH.

BLOOP!

GURR! GNASH! WHAT DO YOU THINK YOU'RE DOING?

PERFECT! JUST PERFECT!

SHORTLY, IN GLEN FUDGE —

HAW! HAW! WE DIDN'T HALF GIVE THE McMINXES A TANKING TODAY!

AAAOOOAAOO!

GULP! WHASSAT?

Chapter Three — Spy in the Sky!

BIG CHIEF FATTY MacFUDGE IS LUNCHING —

THINK I'LL HAVE ANOTHER SWISS ROLL . . .

CHIEFY

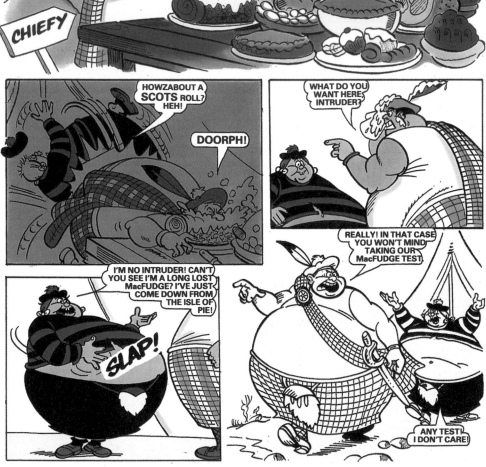

HOWZABOUT A **SCOTS** ROLL? HEH!

DOORPH!

WHAT DO YOU WANT HERE, INTRUDER?

REALLY! IN THAT CASE YOU WON'T MIND TAKING OUR MacFUDGE TEST!

I'M NO INTRUDER! CAN'T YOU SEE I'M A LONG LOST MacFUDGE? I'VE JUST COME DOWN FROM THE ISLE OF PIE!

SLAP!

ANY TEST! I DON'T CARE!

MINNIE FLIPS HER LID!

...THAT FATTY MacFUDGE HAS MADE ME **FIGHTING MAD!** FEED ME TO HIS PET MONSTER, WOULD HE?

LET'S SPIFFLICATE 'EM THIS TIME! UP THE McMINXES!

UH-OH! HERE COME THE McMINXES FOR THEIR DAILY DUFFING!

BREAK OUT THE FIGHTING BREW.

HERE IT IS, CHIEFY.

GLUG!

GLUG!

I CAN FEEL IT WORKING.

WE'RE READY FOR ANYTHING NOW.

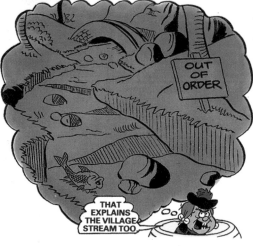